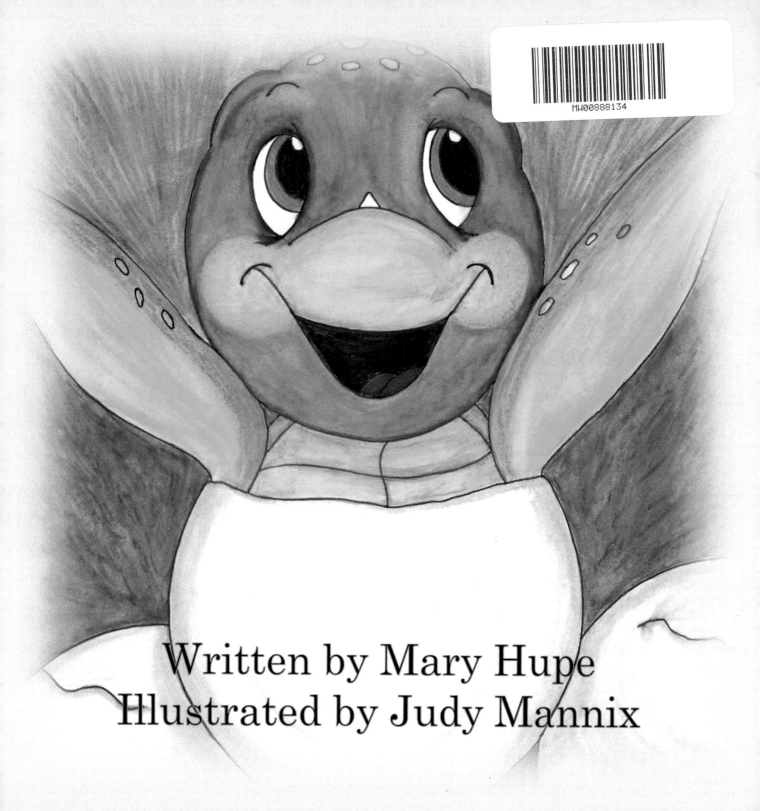

Written by Mary Hupe
Hlustrated by Judy Mannix

Terri's Debut by Mary Hupe
Illustrated by Judy Mannix
Published 2018 by Paidion Publishing, Inc.

Illustrations by: Judy Mannix
Text by: Zsa-Zsa Venter
Book layout by: Paidion Publishing, Inc.

Printed in the United States of America
ISBN-13: 978-1-948116-00-8

Dedication

Thank you to my husband, family
and friends for all your love,
encouragement, and support that
helped make my dream a reality.
Thank you to the students and the
other children in my life who inspire
me every day.

It was really dark
and quiet.

Some weeks ago, my mommy used her gigantic flippers to cover me with sand.

My mommy laid more eggs next to me,
and covered them with sand too.

The darkness and the sand protected
us from predators.

We waited, waited,

and waited...

I heard children playing near me and someone said,
"Stay away from the nest!"

Finally, the time came for me to hatch and make my debut. I used my special tooth to break open my shell.

Yes! I was FREE!

It took a few days to dig and reach the top of the sand.
I had to navigate carefully to not get stuck in the
yellow tape.

The sky was dark, but the bright moonlight guided me
to my home in the ocean.

I used my powerful flippers to travel hundreds of feet
across the sand.
I even have special claws on my flippers that helped me.
I had to move quickly down to the sea so the predators
didn't see me.
It was very scary!

At last, I made it!
I touched the water for the first time and swam out
into the magnificent blue sea!

I felt so free and I loved exploring my new home.

I heard a voice I didn't know saying,
"Hello, my name is Raymond the Reading Ray."

"Hi!
My name is Terri and I'm new here!"

"Welcome home, Terri. I have been living here for five
years," said Raymond.
"Do you want to hang out with me?"

"I would love to!" said Terri.

THE END

Loggerhead Sea Turtle Facts

These reptiles got their name from their oversized head, which looks like a big log.

Their lifespan in the wild is 50+ years.

They can weigh up to 115kg.

They can be up to 90cm long.

They live in oceans all around the world, except in the coldest seas far north and south, near the Earth's poles.

They are omnivores, but they eat mostly jellyfish, mollusks and crustaceans. They use their strong, powerful jaws to crush and eat their prey who have shells.

They have four flippers with two, sometimes three, claws on each one.

They migrate long distances between their feeding grounds and their nesting sites. A female adult turtle may travel over 12,000km back to the beach where she hatched as a baby, and lay her own eggs there!

Serious threats to loggerheads are fishing equipment, pollution, and destruction to their nesting beaches.

Author's Bio

As an Elementary Special Education teacher, Mary Hupe is known for using a creative, fun, and "out of the box" approach to learning. For one, she uses puppets to make lessons and stories lively and engaging. She has made numerous impacts on children, helping to bring out their best, and to see that they each have a special purpose. She encourages them to persevere through challenges and overcome obstacles.

Her love for children and animals has been evident since childhood, where she owned a variety of animals, cared for injured or sick animals in her neighborhood, and performed the role of a teacher to the younger children in her neighborhood. These passions, along with her love for children's books, have culminated into her dream of being an author herself.

Mary Hupe earned a Bachelor's Degree in Human Services and Psychology, and a Master's Degree in Counseling from Assumption College in Worcester, MA. She also received her Elementary Education and Special Education (ESE) certification. She has worked with children for over 20 years in the areas of Education, Counseling, and Social Work.

She resides in St. Cloud, FL with her husband Lud and adorable puppies, Teddy and Sammy. After becoming intrigued with the life cycle of a sea turtle when on a recent trip to the beach during nesting season, she was inspired to write this heart warming story of a hatchling making her debut in this world!

Illustrator's Bio

Judy has been drawing and painting ever since she can remember. One special Christmas she received from Santa a "Learn to Draw with Jon Gnagy" art set and from then on she was hooked. Her love for art continued to grow, and for over 40 years she has created many paintings, murals, and arts and crafts for friends and family. Becoming a children's book illustrator is a dream come true.

In addition to illustrating, Judy has written several picture book manuscripts which she hopes to have published. Expanding her creativity into other areas, Judy is an experienced home baker who regularly creates specialty cakes and confections for clients. Last July, Judy was chosen to audition for the fourth season of The Great American Baking Show in Los Angeles, California.

Judy has been a full time elementary school teacher for 10 years, and is the mother of two adult children and grandmother of two. Married to Bill for 32 years, she lives in Saint Cloud, Florida with her cats Tigger and Simba, who love to steal her paint brushes and curl up on her sketch pads whenever they can.

Contact Info

For illustrations, ghost-writing and speaking
engagements, please contact:

Mary Hupe - amore11572@yahoo.com
Judy Mannix – jmannix818@yahoo.com

For publishing information, please contact Paidion
Publisher. Inc. at paidionpublishing@gmail.com

Made in the USA
Columbia, SC
25 August 2019